To:

From:

SIX DAYS AT CAMP WITH LIN AND JILL

by C. Knebel
Simple Words Books™

Illustrated by M. Perez

FREE WORKBOOKS
and
FREE ACCESS TO ONLINE SUMMITS

simplewordsbooks.com

Day 1 - Sunday
Trip To The Camp

Lin's Day

"Did you pack all you need to bring, Lin?" asks Mrs. Mills.

"I have all of my things in the backpack, Mom," says Lin. "I am all set to go."

"Will Beth and her mom pick you up?" asks Mrs. Mills.

"No, I will go to the inn with the bus," says Lin. "Beth will not be at the inn. Her mom will drop her off at Camp Grit on Monday."

Lin does not like this a bit. "I wish Beth were at the inn with me," she thinks. She picks up her red cap and gets her black vest on. She grabs her backpack and a small bag with snacks and drinks for the trip.

"Let us get to the bus stop on time," says Mrs. Mills and off they go.

At the bus stop, Mrs. Mills hugs Lin.

"Have fun at camp," she says half glad and half sad.

Lin hugs her mom back and adds a kiss.

"Just a day. I will stay out of Jill Finn's grasp. All will be O.K. I can do this," Lin thinks as she gets on the bus.

It is not a quick bus trip to the inn. The sun has set when Lin gets to the inn. She is spent. She just wants to go to bed.

"Hi, Lin," says Miss Gibbs.

Lin jumps in shock. She does not expect Miss Gibbs to be at the check in desk.

Miss Gibbs runs Camp Grit. The kids think she is stiff. But Lin thinks she is fun.

"Be on time for the bus to the camp. You must be at the bus stop by 8:30 a.m.," Miss Gibbs tells her.

Lin gets in the bed. She needs to rest.

"I am glad I did not run into Jill at the inn!" she thinks as she drifts off. "She must be at the inn by now. I bet Jill did not go on a bus to get to the inn like I had to."

Jill's Day

Brush. Check.

Silk dress. Check.

Red lipstick. Check.

It is the last bag. Jill is set for Camp Grit.

"Oh, my!" says Jill's mom, Mrs. Finn. "Six bags? Six bags are a lot!"

"No, it is not," grins Jill. A bag a day. Six days at camp sum up to six bags. I can pack six more, Mom."

"Yes, Jill. You can pack six more bags. But you will not," Mrs. Finn grins back. "Miss Gibbs will be at the inn when you get there. She will get you and the rest of the kids to the camp on Monday," she adds.

Honk! Honk!

A tall man with a black hat gets out of a black van.

"Time to go! The van to pick you up is in front," calls Jill's dad. "Let us go."

"Be quick. Go! Go!" says Jill's mom.

Jill runs down the steps with no bags. Mrs. Finn has to drag them all. Mr. Finn runs up the steps to help with the bags.

"Is it just me," Mrs. Finn asks, "or is this a lot of bags for six days? Do you think they will fit in the trunk of the van?"

Mr. Finn shrugs. "That is our Jill. Six bags do not shock me. Let me check if we can fit them in the trunk."

The man with the black hat helps Mr. Finn bring the bags out to the van. Mr. Finn tips the man well when he fits all of the bags into the trunk.

"The van is all set to go to the inn. We will be at the camp the last day to pick you up. It is in just six days," says Mr. Finn.

Mrs. Finn asks, "Where is my hug, pumpkin?"

Jill hugs her mom and dad. Then she runs out.

"Text me when you get to the inn," tells Mrs. Finn. "Have fun at camp."

The man with the black hat helps Jill into the van.

"I will!" Jill yells as she jumps in the back of the van.

She is glad to be on her way to the inn. She thinks of how much fun the next six days will be. But what if Lin is at the camp as well? Six days with Lin Mills...

"Sid and my fans will be at the camp. If Lin Mills will be at Camp Grit, she will just be a speck for me. How bad can it be?" Jill thinks.

Day 2 - Monday
Camp Grit

Lin's Day

Lin is set to get on the bus at 8:15 a.m. She sits all the way at the back as if she wants to blend into the bus.

Jill and Sid are the last to get on the bus. Jill sits in the front with Sid. Lin ducks down as much as she can so they will not spot her in the back of the bus.

"At last, we are out of the inn and on our way to camp. Beth must be at the camp by now," thinks Lin.

It is a quick trip from the inn to Camp Grit. When the bus gets there, Beth is by the van with her mom. Lin jumps off the bus and runs to Beth.

"Hi, Mrs. Rand," says Lin.

"Did you miss me?" asks Beth with a grin.

"You bet I did. Lots and lots!" Lin hugs Beth.

Lin and Beth pick up their bags.

As Beth's mom sets off, a small black cat sprints by Beth. Lin jumps and drops her bag. She cannot stand black cats.

When Lin was six, a black cat split her best doll in half. From then on, black cats are on Lin's black list.

"You and black cats," says Beth. "But this is such a small cat, Lin."

"Small black cats are still black cats. They are bad luck. Just hang on. It may not be just yet, but they all bring bad luck. This camp will not end well," Lin says to Beth.

"Oh, stop it," kids Beth.

Brrring! Brrring! Brrring!

Miss Gibbs rings the camp bell to bring all the kids next to her.

"That is Miss Gibbs. Let us run," Lin grabs Beth's hand.

They pick a spot next to Miss Gibbs.

"Glad to have you at Camp Grit," says Miss Gibbs.

"Hi, Miss Gibbs," the kids yell.

"Fact 1: No tablets or calls for the rest of the camp," says Miss Gibbs. "All tablets must be off until the end of the camp."

All the kids are sad, but not Lin. She does not have a tablet or a thing to send texts with. She is glad she will not be left out.

"Fact 2: You will have a job to do at camp. The lists of tasks are in your huts. And I trust you will check out the lists by the end of the day," says Miss Gibbs.

"This is not a day camp. You will be in a club for the stay. You will stay in the huts with the kids in your club. We have ten clubs in the camp. There are six in a club. When I call you, pick up all your bags. Go to your huts to drop them off. You can unpack if you want. Then grab lunch. Be quick or not much will be left to snack on," Miss Gibbs adds.

Then she calls the clubs.

"Club Sun:

Jan King.

Jill Finn.

Viv Frank.

Fran Hill.

Sid Buck."

"Not Club Sun. Not Club Sun. Not for me," thinks Lin.

"and Lin Mills," adds Miss Gibbs.

"How can this be?" thinks Lin. She is sad to be stuck with Jill and Sid. And not be with Beth.

Beth ends up in Club Run. Lin asks Miss Gibbs if she can stay with Beth in Club Run's hut. But no luck. Miss Gibbs will not let her. Lin has to stay with Club Sun until the end of camp.

"This is no fun," she grunts.

Lin looks at Jill. Jill nags that she got no help with her bags.

"We just got to camp," Lin thinks. "And Jill nags that she has to pick up her bags. No shock there. That is how Jill is. Nag, nag, nag..."

Lin picks up her backpack. She is fast to go to the hut so she does not have to help Jill.

She likes the hut. It is small and has bunk beds. It is a bit hot, but not that bad.

"Jill will not last a day in this hut," Lin thinks with a grin.

She casts her bag on the bed on top of Fran's and next to Jan's and Viv's. This way, Jill and Sid will not be in the beds next to Lin's.

Jill still nags as she gets into the hut. This time she says she does not like the hut.

"Her mom cannot pay for a big hut. Is that why we stay in such a small shed?" she adds.

Lin acts as if she does not get what Jill says. But she does. She cannot stand Jill when she brags how rich she is.

Jill just does not stop. Then she looks at Lin and adds, "This hut stinks. It smells like fish. Yuck!"

Beth is quick to visit Lin's hut. She thinks Lin must be sad to be in Club Sun with Jill. Beth gets this. She does not like Jill at all. Not like she did in the past.

"I am on egg shells when I am with Jill. She is such a snob. I want to go back to my mom," Lin tells Beth.

Beth hugs Lin. Lin hugs her back.

"Do not let her get to you. We will have a lot of fun. You will not be in the hut with her that much. We will be out all day," Beth tells Lin. "Let us go to lunch and have fun. We will spend the rest of the day out of Jill's grasp."

And that is just what they do.

At bed time, Lin checks the job list.

Lin Mills: Set up Cabin 101 and Cabin 102 by 10 a.m. for Rock Band Gig prep.

"Not bad," she thinks. She sets her drum sticks next to her cap. She is set for the big day.

Jill's Day

"Sun is up!" Jill sings to Sid, who is still in bed.

"Stop it, Jill. I do not want to get out of bed yet. What time is it?" asks Sid.

"Time to get up and go to the bus stop," Jill says. "Get up, Sid. Just do as I tell you!"

"Just tell me. What time is it?" asks Sid.

"It is 8:15!" says Jill.

"What? 8:15! I do not have time to brush and fix... I must be quick."

"Yes, you must," hums Jill. "Yes, you must."

Sid thinks Jill is her best pal. But Jill acts as if Sid is more like a big fan than a best pal. Sid likes to go by what Jill says all the time.

Jill and Sid get to the bus stop just in time. Jill grabs a spot in the front. Sid sits next to her.

Jill spots Lin on the bus. "There is Lin. I am glad she is at the back of the bus and out of my way. Look at her. She is such a mess."

When they get to the camp, Beth stands by her mom's van. Jill and Beth had a lot of fun in that van when they were six. They were best pals back then. But that is in the past. Yet, Jill still feels sad to miss Beth so much.

All the kids get off the bus. A small black cat runs in front of Beth's mom's van. Lin jumps when the cat runs by her. Jill can tell that Lin still panics if a black cat is by her.

"Lin and black cats," thinks Jill.

The camp bell rings. All kids run to Miss Gibbs.

"Fact 1: No tablets or calls for the rest of the camp," tells Miss Gibbs.

"No texts?" Fran asks in shock.

"No i-pads or i-pods?"

Jill and Sid wish to have Fran in their club. She is so much fun.

"No calls! No texts! No tablets! Got it?" grins Miss Gibbs.

Jill does not like this a bit.

"Fact 2: You will have a job to do at camp. The lists of tasks are in your huts. I trust you will check out the lists by end of the day," says Miss Gibbs.

"You will be in a club. We have ten clubs in the camp. There are six in a club," Miss Gibbs tells the kids. "You will stay in the huts with the kids in your club."

Then, she picks the Camp Clubs.

Jill is in Club Sun. So is Sid.

They are glad not to be split up. They clap as they jump. But Lin is in that hut as well!

It is time to go to the huts. But how? Jill has six bags. She has to bring all of them to the hut. This will be a big job.

All the kids have lots of bags to bring. All but Lin. Lin has just a backpack and not a thing in her hands. But she does not want to help Jill. She picks up her bag fast and she is off to the hut.

Jill gets upset with Lin.

"Who does she think she is?" Jill grunts. "I do not need Lin's help!"

But Jill does need help.

"Is there no camp staff to bring my bags to the hut?" she nags.

"Camp Grit is a self-help camp, Jill!" snaps Miss Gibbs. "Get your bags! Chop chop!"

Jill grabs her bags. But she cannot get it all. She drags half of the bags to the hut. She is upset that she has to go back to pick up the rest.

Jill is last to the hut. She checks it out. "Bunk beds!" she yelps. The last bed is up top. It has a big lump. It is not snug at all.

Jill does not like the hut a bit. "This is not a hut. It is a small shed. Just a step up from a tent. There must be a mix up. My dad did not spend this much cash for me to stay in this shed," she says.

She is still mad at Lin. She wants her to be sad.

She looks at Lin and says, "Her mom cannot pay for a big hut. Is that why we stay in such a small shed?"

Jill spins with her hand on her hip and adds, "This hut stinks. It smells like bad fish. Yuck. And it is so hot. Is there an AC in the hut? Is it on?"

"Stop it, Jill!" Miss Gibbs cuts in. She is not glad that Jill says such things.

Jill does not check the task list. She does not want a job.

Sid looks at the list. "Jill, will you check your job?" she asks.

Jill shrugs. "What is your job?"

"Rock Band Gig trash pick up. I have to do it the next day," says Sid.

"What is Lin's job?" Jill asks.

"Lin's? Well, she has to set up Cabin 101 and Cabin 102 by 10 a.m. for Rock Band Gig prep."

Sid checks Jill's task and says, "The day of the Grand Ball will be hectic for you."

"Is it my job?" asks Jill. "What is it?"

"Grand Ball set up," Sid tells her. "That is a big job. And you will want to get set for the ball as well."

Jill thinks Grand Ball set up is not bad at all. She is glad she does not have to pick up trash.

"Let us get out of this shed and have fun," she tells Sid.

Jill and Sid run out of the hut. They have lunch and spend the rest of the day by the clay stand. Jill crafts a clay pup and a cat. She thinks her mom and dad will like the clay pup. Sid crafts a mug for her dad and a pot for her mom.

The day ends fast with no big mess.

Day 3 - Tuesday
Rock Band Gig

Lin's Day

It is Rock Band Gig day.

Lin is up with the sun. She jumps out of the bed. She slips into her black pants and a red top as fast as she can.

She grabs her red cap and picks up her drum sticks on her way out.

She runs to Beth's hut. All the kids are still in bed in Club Run's hut. But not Beth. She is all set.

"It is the big Rock Band Gig Day! This is EPIC! Rock Band Rocks! Rock Band Rocks!" Lin and Beth chant.

"Shh! We are still in bed," yell the rest of the Club Run with a grunt.

Lin and Beth rush to Cabin 101 and Cabin 102. They want to check off their jobs on the list and get on with the day. So they set it all up fast.

The 10 a.m. class is for the band whiz. It is no shock that Lin and Beth are in that class. They like to play the drums. And they play well. They are the best in the camp.

There are lots of kids in this class. Sid is in this class as well. But not Jill.

Miss Gibbs asks the class, "Are you all set with your act for the Rock Band Gig?"

Lin and Beth yell, "Yes. We will play 'I Got You'."

"That is a fantastic pick," Miss Gibbs tells them.

Beth and Lin are quick to get on with their act.

"What a splendid job," claps Miss Gibbs when their act ends. "You play so well."

Next, Sid plays the clarinet. Her act does not go well. She still needs help.

Lin and Beth help Sid and the rest of the kids in the class. Lin thinks that Sid does not like the help. It is as if Sid does not trust Lin.

Miss Gibbs thanks Lin and Beth for their help with the class.

"Can we be the last to go, Miss Gibbs?" asks Beth.

"I trust that you will play as well as you did in the class. Plus, you help the rest of the class. You are like my backup. You can be the last to go!" grins Miss Gibbs.

Lin and Beth jump and clap. "We are Top Gun. We got this!" says Lin.

"Yes. But this Top Gun has to get gas so it does not crash," says Beth with a grin. "Let us grab a quick lunch. Or I will pass out."

On their way out, they run into Jill in Cabin 102. Jill has a gong in her hand.

"Gong? You will play the gong? Not a bad pick. You need no skills for that," says Lin to Jill.

It was not her plan to say this. But it is out of her lips now. Lin and Beth run out of the class fast. But they bet Jill is upset with them.

Lin and Beth have lunch on the grass.

"Do you want to play chess with us?" Fran asks Beth and Lin.

Beth likes to play chess. But she thinks Jill and Sid may be there as well.

"Thanks, Fran. I think we will skip chess. Plus, we have to do our act a last time," says Beth. Lin and Beth are set for their act. They play just a bit more so they can be at their best.

The sun sets and it is time for the Rock Band Gig!

Beth and Lin go last. They play so well. It is spot on! This is such a thrill. They all have a blast.

The Rock Band Gig is a big hit. This is the best day at camp for Lin and Beth!

Jill's Day

It is Rock Band Gig day. This is not Jill's best day at the camp. She is not into the band stuff. She has no skills to play in a band.

Jill thinks Beth and Lin play the drums well. She cannot stand that. She wants to crush the Rock Band Gig for them.

"What are you up to, Jill?" asks Sid.

"Let us play a prank on Lin and Beth," Jill half kids to test what Sid will say. "What do you think?"

Sid does not say a thing. She does not like it when Jill acts like this. She does not want to play pranks. This plan is not for her.

"Hi, kids!" says Miss Gibbs as she gets in the hut.

Jill jumps when Miss Gibbs pops up next to her.

"Oh, that was bad. Do you think Miss Gibbs got that?" she asks Sid.

Sid shrugs. Pranks are not her thing. But she still does not say a thing to Jill.

Miss Gibbs hands the kids their time slots for the Rock Band Gig prep. "Sid, you have the 10 a.m. slot in Cabin 101. Jill, you are at 11 a.m. in Cabin 102."

"Time to go. I got the 10 a.m. slot," yells Sid as she grabs her clarinet and sprints out of the hut. She just wants to get out of there.

Sid is glad to be at the 10 a.m. class with the best band. She plays the clarinet well. But she still needs a bit of help.

Lin and Beth help Sid with her act. Sid is glad for the help. But she does not get why they want to help her. Jill says Lin and Beth are bad, so Sid expects them to be bad. But now she thinks Jill may be just as bad with her pranks and all.

At the end of the class, Sid packs her clarinet in its box to bring it with her. She wants to play a bit more when lunch ends so she can do her best at the gig.

She sprints out fast not to bump into Jill. She thinks Jill must be mad that Sid is not at the 11 a.m. class with her.

Sid runs to the pond. She sits on a rock with a rod.

"Can I fish with you?" asks Jan. She sits on a rock next to Sid. All the kids like Jan. She is fun.

Back at the hut, Jill checks the clock on the wall. It is just 10:45.

"I do not like this band stuff. There must be a way to get out of this gig," she thinks. "I wish Sid was in this class with me."

Jill gets to Cabin 102 at 10:50 a.m. She still does not have a thing to play. That just kills her. She likes to be the best in all she does.

She checks the list on the wall. This does not look good.

Trumpet. No!

Clarinet. No!

Drums. No!

Then, she spots it!

The list says, "Gong: No skill to play and quick to get the hang of."

"This is for me," thinks Jill.

She digs into the stack. She grabs the big brass gong and a stick that is next to it.

Just then, Lin and Beth pass by Cabin 102. Jill is in the class with a gong in her hand.

"Gong? Not a bad pick. You need no skills for that," says Lin and they run out.

"That is it! I will play a prank on Lin and Beth. They will go down at the Rock Band Gig."

But what trick? Jill has to map this out well.

At 11:05, the rest of the kids are in the class. They are all set to play.

"This slot is for you if you are not a band whiz," tells Miss Gibbs.

"Yuck! It is by skill. I bet Lin and Beth were with Sid. I cannot stand that I am stuck with this class!" grunts Jill.

"Can you play the gong, Jill?" asks Miss Gibbs.

"Not yet," Jill says.

"Did you play the gong in the past?" Miss Gibbs asks.

Jill says no. Then, she hits the gong with the stick.

Bong! Bong! Bong!

"Jill, can you step it up just a bit?"

asks Miss Gibbs. She thinks Jill cannot be this bad.

"This is my best. Trust me on this," says Jill. But this is not her best. Not at all.

"Oh, my!" thinks Miss Gibbs.

"Can I skip the Rock Band Gig?" Jill asks. This is her shot to get out of the gig.

Miss Gibbs frets what the gig will be like if Jill is there. Not just her lack of skills. Jill will be mad that she is not the best. The rest will have to pay for it. A mad Jill is not what Miss Gibbs wants at the gig.

"In fact, Jill, yes. It will be best if you skip the Rock Band Gig. But then you will get a big task on the day of the Grand Ball. You will have to help with the set up for the ball. If you can do that, you can skip the Rock Band Gig. Think and pick: the Grand Ball set up or the Rock Band Gig," says Miss Gibbs.

Set up for the ball is Jill's job on the list. This does not add more for her to do. But she will not tell that to Miss Gibbs.

"I do not have to think. Grand Ball set up it is. I will be glad to help. Am I out of the Rock Band Gig?" Jill asks.

Miss Gibbs nods.

She gets back the brass gong from Jill still intact.

"You can go now, Jill. But do not forget the set up for the Grand Ball."

She lets Jill out of the class.

Jill is glad to get out of the Rock Band Gig. On her way out, she spots Lin and Beth in Cabin 101. They play the drums and have fun.

"I miss the fun Beth and I had," Jill thinks as she gets out.

But she forgets Beth fast when she spots Sid by the pond. She is not glad that Jan sits with Sid. She cuts in their chat. And the fun ends for Sid.

"Is that a rod in your hand? Will you fish? Are you nuts?" Jill yells at Sid. "This stinks!"

Sid is not glad that Jill is out of the class this quick. She just got to the pond. She drops the rod and stands up in a rush. Just one more thing that Sid likes but cannot do, thanks to Jill. She picks up the rod and hands it to Jan.

Jill tells Sid that Miss Gibbs let her skip the Rock Band Gig. She tells Sid to skip the gig as well.

Sid wants to be in the gig. But she cannot tell this to Jill. So she says that Miss Gibbs will not let her skip as well.

"Plus, there is not much time left until the gig. I must play my clarinet just a bit more," says Sid.

"No way," says Jill. "Let us play chess."

She grabs Sid's hand. Sid's clarinet stays in its box until the gig.

Jill and Sid hang out with Fran and play chess.

Fran sits at a desk next to Sid. She checks Sid's chess steps when Sid plays with Jill.

"Check what time it is, Sid," Fran says as she cuts in.

"Time for the gig!" Sid gets up fast.

"We have to be on time." Fran grabs Sid's hand. "Let us go."

Sid picks up her clarinet and runs with Fran.

"Sid, get back to the hut quick when your act ends. I will be there," Jill yells.

On the way to the gig, Fran asks Sid, "What did you do with your King back there?"

Sid shrugs.

"Why do you let Jill win like this all the time? I do not get it. You have to get out of your shell and stand up to Jill."

"It is just chess, Fran. Not a big thing," says Sid. She wants to brush it off.

At the gig, Sid does not play as well as she wants. It is not her best.

She is in and out of the Rock Band Gig quick to hang out with Jill in the hut. She does not get to check out the rest of the acts.

In the hut, Jill and Sid plan for the Grand Ball. This is fun for Sid. This is the Jill she likes. And Jill forgets to play a prank on Lin.

The day ends with no tricks.

Day 4 - Wednesday
Grand Ball

Lin's Day

Jill and Sid chat on Sid's bed. They are as glad as can be.

The sun is just up. "Shh," thinks Lin. She had a hectic day with the Rock Band Gig. She wants to rest just a bit more.

"Oh, no! It is the day of the Grand Ball," Lin thinks. "I will not have a dress on. No way!" She looks at Jill and Sid. The Grand Ball is Jill's thing.

When Beth gets to Lin's hut, Lin is set to go out. She has no intent to be in the hut when Jill and Sid prep for the ball.

"It is a gray day. I get sad when the sun is not out," Lin says to Beth.

Beth still has the thrill of the Rock Band Gig. "We just had the best gig. You cannot be down. Let us go have fun."

Lin grins. "You got it! Do you think we can top the Rock Band Gig?" Her spirit is back.

Beth nods, "You bet we can!"

Lin and Beth do not have much to do until the ball. So they play chess. They are not the best at chess, but they still like to play it. They are up for ping pong as well.

When they are spent, they grab lunch. They bring their fish and chips to the pond and have a picnic on the grass. They plan to hang out there for the rest of the day until the ball.

A small cat hangs out by the pond as well. He smells Beth's lunch. He wants to snack on the fish. The cat jumps on Beth's lap. Beth pats its back.

"Lin, check out this cat," says Beth. "Think he wants my lunch?"

"A black cat?" Lin gasps. She is quick to step back. "That is bad luck, Beth. Get him off your lap."

"Bad luck? A gray day with a black cat. This will be a day from hell," kids Beth with a grin.

Lin does not grin back. She has a bad hunch. But she cannot tell what it is.

Just as the cat jumps off Beth's lap, Sid runs by them.

"Was that Sid?" asks Beth.

"Yes. And I think she is sad," says Lin.

"Do you think we can help her?" asks Beth.

They go to the bench to check on Sid.

"Are you O.K.?" asks Lin.

"Yes," Sid sniffs. But she is not well in fact. "It is just Jill," she adds.

"I do not get why you hang out with Jill," says Lin. "You are not like her at all."

"I ask that same thing on days like this. She is not that bad. Well, not all the time. And I like to hang out with her when it is just Jill and me," says Sid.

"Your dress is a hit. You are set for the Grand Ball," Beth jumps in the chat! She wants to get a grin out of Sid. "Just forget Jill. Let us get the rods and we can fish. Do you like to fish?"

Sid nods. "In this dress?" she asks.

"So what," Lin grins. "A bit of fun with us may just be what you need."

"Well… Let us fish then!" Sid is glad.

"I have a plan," Lin says. "We can hang out by the pond until the ball."

"And you can go to the ball with us if you want," adds Beth.

Sid is in shock. "You want to go to the Grand Ball with me? But why?"

"We get what it is like to be mad at Jill," says Beth.

"You are all set to go to the ball.

Beth and I will dress like this in our pants and caps. We do not have to go back to the huts," winks Lin.

"And all will be O.K., Sid. Chin up," Beth says.

They fish by the pond until the ball. They chat and have fun. Sid does not think of Jill. She forgets that she was mad at her.

At the ball, Beth, Lin and Sid hang out by the drink stand. They kid and have fun until Jill gets there.

Jill is quick to bash the fun.

"There you are at last," Jill says to Sid as she grabs a glass of punch. She has her bag with her.

Lin just wants Jill to chill out. But no luck. They grab bags of chips and act as if Jill is not there.

"Sid, are you with these pests?" she snaps. "Look at them. What a buzz kill. It is no shock that Lin and Beth have pants and caps on. You all look so bad. Were you at the pond? You smell like fish," Jill blasts. "We are at the Grand Ball not…"

"… at the Flat Ball," say Lin and the rest.

They all crack up.

"Is that the best you got, Lin? Ha ha. You do not have the class for a Grand Ball." Jill gets mad.

"Just stop it!" Lin yells back.

In a flash, a black cat jumps out of Jill's bag on to Lin's lap. Lin does not expect that. She yelps and steps back in a panic. She hits the drink stand.

Splash!

Lin trips and lands flat on her back in the punch. She is all wet. Red punch drips from her hands as she stands up. Chips and nuts are stuck to her pants.

What a mess.

Lin gets mad. She looks for Jill, but she is not there. Lin runs out to track her down.

Jill is out on the grass. She sits in the mud with a rip in her dress.

"You will pay for this," yells Jill.

"Bring it on!" Lin yells back.

All the kids and Miss Gibbs run out of the Grand Ball.

"Oh, my! What is this mess?" asks Miss Gibbs.

"Miss Gibbs. It was Jill, not me. Look what she did to me. I fell in the punch when...," yells Lin.

"Lin got me into the mud. My dress is trash," yells Jill.

"What do you think this is? Cut it out! Where is your camp spirit?" Miss Gibbs yells back. "Lin! Jill! Go to your hut! And get a hot bath to get rid of all that punch and mud. Stay in the hut until I get there. We will discuss this when the sun is up. And the rest of you, go back in. On with the Grand Ball."

Beth grabs Sid's hand and says, "Miss Gibbs does not yell at us! She must be mad!"

Lin can tell Miss Gibbs is mad. Lin looks at Beth. Beth shrugs at Lin with half a grin.

Lin runs to the hut. She gets into fresh PJs. She slips into her bed and does not say a thing to Jill. She is sad that Miss Gibbs is mad at her.

"Miss Gibbs may forget all this when the sun is up. She may let this all go," thinks Lin. She is mad at Jill. "If Jill was not at camp with me..." she thinks as she drifts off.

Jill's Day

At last, it is the day of the Grand Ball. This is the best day of the camp for Jill. She gets to dress up.

Jill jumps out of bed with no fuss. She runs to Sid. They chat in Sid's bed and say how much fun they will have at the ball.

Sid is glad it is the Grand Ball Day. Just like Jill, she likes to dress up as well.

"We have to finish our jobs fast," says Jill. "I have to set up for the ball."

"And I will pick up the trash," adds Sid.

"And I will have the best outfit at the ball," grins Jill.

Sid shrugs. She does not get why Jill has to be the best in all she does.

Jill skips and hops from a thing to the next until lunch. She cannot stay still. She just wants to get her dress on. But she has to hang on until it is time.

The set up of the Grand Ball is hectic for her. Yet, she is quick to finish her tasks. She checks things one last time.

When Miss Gibbs gets there, all is set. She did not expect the set up to go this well. There is not a speck of dust. "Good job, Jill. Go and have lunch. Then, you can go to your hut."

Jill sprints out to grab Sid. Sid is all set with the trash pick up as well. There was not much trash at all.

They rush to finish their lunch. They run to the hut as they gulp down the last bit.

To dress up for the Grand Ball is so much fun for Jill and Beth.

Jill sings as she slips into her red silk dress. Sid helps Jill with her red blush and lipstick. Red blush is a fresh look on Jill.

Sid has a pink dress. She likes how it looks on her. But not Jill.

"A hot pink dress? No way, Sid," snaps Jill. "Did you pick up this dress?"

Sid nods.

"Is this the best you can do? I am your best pal, Sid. And I will tell you as it is. This dress does not look good on you. In fact, it looks bad. This is the Grand Ball, not the Flat Ball!" Then she adds, "Check out my red silk dress. It looks so good on me."

Sid stands still in shock. She is sad that Jill does not like her dress. Why does she say such things? And in such a bad way! Sid cannot stand this.

This is the last drop for her.

"Stop it, Jill! I do not like it when you say such bad things to me," Sid snaps back.

"You are such a big brat, Sid," Jill yells back. She is upset that Sid stands up to her.

Sid runs out of the hut fast. She does not look back. She sobs as she runs by Lin and Beth.

Sid sits on a bench by the pond. Lin and Beth sit on the grass next to her. They want to help her. This stuns Sid.

Sid is upset with Jill. But she does not want to say much. And she does not have to.

She is glad Lin and Beth sat next to her. They are not the nut jobs Jill says they are.

Jill gets out the hut to check where Sid went. And there is Sid with Lin and Beth by the pond.

"Lin will not win Sid as well. She will pay for this. How can they stab me in the back like this? I will crush Lin!" grunts Jill.

Jill runs back to the hut. There is a small black cat next to it!

"Lin will flip out if a black cat jumps on her." Jill pets the cat and picks him up. "This cat will do the trick."

Jill brings the cat to Cabin 102. She stays there until the sunset. She does not want Miss Gibbs to get wind of her plan.

When it is time for the ball, Jill grabs the black cat and sets him in her hand bag. "Now, I am all set for the Grand Ball."

When she gets to the ball, the set up is just as she left it. Then she spots Lin, Beth and Sid by the drinks. Jill steps to the drink stand and grabs a glass of punch.

"Sid, are you with these pests?" she snaps. "Were you at the pond? You smell like fish," Jill blasts. "We are at the Grand Ball not…"

"… at the Flat Ball," Lin and the rest finish it for Jill.

"Is that the best you got, Lin? Ha ha. You do not have the class for a Grand Ball." Jill gets as red as her dress.

Red hot mad.

"Just stop it!" yells Lin.

The yells get the cat frantic. He jumps out of Jill's hand bag and on to Lin's lap. Lin yells, "Ahh," as she falls into the punch dish with a big splash. It is a big mess.

"Oh, no! What did I do?" thinks Jill. This was not her plan. But there is no way back now.

Jill runs out fast. She trips on a rock and falls into the mud. Her silk dress gets stuck in the rock and rips. She flips out. This Grand Ball is not fun at all.

When Jill looks up, Lin is next to her. Jill and Lin just yell and yell.

Sid, Beth, Fran, Jan, Viv... all the kids rush out.

And so does Miss Gibbs.

"Cut it out! Where is your camp spirit?" Miss Gibbs yells back at Lin and Jill. "Go to your hut! Stay in the hut until I get there when the sun is up. We will discuss this then," she adds.

The kids are in shock. All stand still. Jill is sad. She did not expect the Grand Ball to end like this.

The rest of the kids get to stay at the ball and have fun. But Lin and Jill have to be in their hut. They scrub the mud and the punch off of them. What a mess this is.

Jill sits on her bed and thinks how much she wants to be at the Grand Ball. But she is stuck in the hut. With Lin Mills.

Day 5 - Tuesday

Stuck With You

The sun is just up. Miss Gibbs is at the hut. She did not forget a thing.

Jill wants to stay in bed. She acts like she needs to rest. Miss Gibbs bangs on her bunk bed.

"Jill, get out of bed. Be quick! To Cabin 101. Chop chop!"

Jill and Lin jump out of their beds. They rush out of the hut fast still in their PJs. They get to Cabin 101 and sit at the desks.

Miss Gibbs is still mad at Jill and Lin.

"But Miss Gibbs. It was Lin, not me," Jill nags. "She is such a…"

"Me? What did I do to you?" yells Lin.

"I will not let you act like this in my camp. Bring back your camp spirit!" Miss Gibbs has a grim look. "You will not get out of this cabin until you bring this to an end. Got it?"

"But it is the Club Day…" says Jill.

"No Club Day for you or you." Miss Gibbs is direct.

This is no trick. Jill and Lin are stuck in this cabin.

"All day?" asks Jill.

"All day if you must. That is up to you," says Miss Gibbs.

Lin and Jill nod.

They have no say in this.

"I trust you will fix this," says Miss Gibbs. "I left snacks and drinks at the back if you have to spend the rest of the day in this cabin," she adds as she exits the cabin.

Jill and Lin sit at the desks. Not a thing from Jill. Not a thing from Lin.

There is not much to say.

The clock ticks. But it is as if time stands still.

Lin stands up and looks at the flags on the string to pass the time.

Jill just cannot sit still and not say a thing. "Of all the kids, I had to be stuck with Lin Mills," she says as she checks out the snacks.

Jill grabs a bag of chips and a drink. Then she sits back at her desk.

"Are you glad that I will miss the Club Day?" she asks. "I am so fed up with you!"

"What did I do? It was you! You had the cat in your bag. It was your plan that got us stuck in this cabin," Lin snaps.

"You are such an odd duck, Lin!" Jill snaps back. "I cannot stand that I have to spend the day stuck with you in this cabin. There is no way out!"

"There is a way out. We can bring this to an end," hints Lin.

Jill shrugs. "You think you have it all, Lin. But you do not!"

"I cannot stand this, Jill. Just stop the fuss! Why do you have to be this way?" Lin cracks.

She wants to yell, "I AM SICK OF JILL FINN," at the top of her lungs. But she stops.

"I will not go down this path. She cannot drag me down with her. Not this time," she thinks.

"Why are you like this to me?" Lin calls her out.

"What way?" Jill does not expect Lin to ask her stuff like this.

"As if I do not exist," Lin sits down at the desk next to Jill.

"You do not, Lin. Not for me," Jill tells Lin. "Does this shock you? Does it?" she snaps.

Lin gets the chills. "No. It does not. Not a bit. You are glad when I slip up," says Lin. "It is O.K. to think you are the best. But do not think less of me."

"I am mad that you got all the best things. The things that I want but I do not have."

"Like what?" Lin asks in a shock.

She thinks Jill is the rich kid. What does Lin have that Jill does not?

Jill wants to brush it off. "I kept a lid on it for all this time. I will not let it all out now."

"Be frank for a sec, will you Jill!" grunts Lin.

"Band, math… and… Beth!" These rush out of Jill's lips.

"Say what?" asks Lin. "Beth?"

"I still get mad when I think of the day I met you. We were Jill and Beth. J & B. We were best pals. Until you got in our fun. With you, it was "Let us run. Let us jump. Let us swim." I did not want to do all that. But Beth did! Then, she forgot me."

"Did I rob you of Beth?" Lin asks in shock.

"I still miss Beth. I miss her a lot. But now she is with you all the time. She runs with you. She jumps with you. She swims with you. And she does not do a thing with me. That is why I do not like you!"

This stuns Lin. "But we were just six back then. We were small kids."

"Beth and I had a pact. Then you just trash our pact in a blink!" Jill is sad." She left me for you. She was my best pal back then. Now, she is your best pal. And I do not have one."

"Is Sid not your best pal?" asks Lin.

"No! Well, yes. She may be. Is she?" Jill stops and thinks. Sid stands by her. She sticks up for her. Jill trusts her. And Sid trusts Jill. Still, she does not think of Sid that way. But in fact, she is.

Jill feels stuck up. "I am such a brat. Did I not call Sid a brat? She must be mad at me. What did I do?"

"You and Sid will be O.K.," says Lin as she pats Jill's hand.

"You think so?" asks Jill.

"Yes. I can bet on it," Lin grins. "And we will fix things with Beth as well. The pact will be back on. Just with more of us!"

"Thank you!" says Jill and hugs Lin. "It is as if a big rock is off my chest."

"Look at us. This is big stuff," Lin says.

Jill nods.

They chat until the sun sets. It gets dim in the cabin.

"Where did the day go?" asks Jill.

"I did not expect the day to end this way. Not at all. But I am glad it did. And I had fun," says Lin.

Jill nods. "Let us check what Sid and Beth are up to."

In the hut, Sid asks Beth, "Are they still in that cabin? It is 5:30 p.m. We must tell Miss Gibbs that Lin and Jill did not get out of the cabin yet."

Just as she says this, Jill and Lin exit the cabin hand in hand still in their PJs.

"Can that be Lin and Jill? Sid, pinch me!" says Beth in shock.

Beth and Sid run to Lin and Jill. The kids chat at the swing set until it is time for bed. Now they are one big gang!

Day 6 - Friday
The Last Day of Camp

"Last bag. Just have to zip it and I am all set," says Jill. "

All six?" asks Sid with a grin. "Hand me a bag. I will help you."

"Let me help you with your bags as well," says Lin. Her bag is on her back and she grabs some of Jill's.

Jill stops Lin. "I got a small gift for you."

"A gift?" asks Lin.

This stuns her. What can it be?

Jill gets out a black clay cat and hands it to Lin. There is a tag on it. It says: "To Lin, From Jill. A black cat can bring you luck!"

"This was my best craft at camp," says Jill. "And I want you to have it."

"Thanks," grins Lin. "Black cats are off my black list. And that is a fact."

Beth gets to the Club Sun's hut. She helps with the rest of Jill's bags. The gang gets to the lot where the moms and dads pick up the kids.

Lin and Beth hand Jill's bags to Mr. Finn.

"You got the best pals to help you with all these bags," Mr. Finn tells Jill.

"Yes, Dad. They are the best pals I can ask for."

"Did you have fun at the Grand Ball?" asks Jill's mom.

"More or less. It was a ball I will not forget," Jill winks at Lin.

Beth's and Lin's moms are by Beth's mom's van. Beth hugs her mom.

"Hi, Mrs. Rand," says Jill.

"Jill, is that you? Look how big you got," says Mrs. Rand. "Did you get to spend time with Beth at camp? I bet she must miss you. Visit us, will you?"

Jill grins. "I will stop by, Mrs. Rand. You can bet on it."

"How was camp?" asks Lin's mom.

"It was a camp I will not forget," says Lin. She winks back at Jill.

Jill, Lin, Beth and Sid hug one last time.

What a six days at camp it was!

You can download full color

CERTIFICATE OF ACCOMPLISHMENT
and
CERTIFICATE OF COMPLETION

on our website

SIMPLEWORDSBOOKS.COM

Certificate of Accomplishment

This certificate is awarded to

_____

for successful completion of

Six Days At Camp with Lin and Jill

_____ _____
Signature   Date

SIMPLE WORDS

WORD LIST
FOR
SIX DAYS AT CAMP
WITH LIN AND JILL

#	Word	Count	#	Word	Count	#	Word	Count
1	a	175	31	beds	4	61	cabin	25
2	a.m.	11	32	bell	2	62	call	2
3	AC	1	33	bench	2	63	calls	6
4	act	10	34	best	34	64	camp	48
5	acts	5	35	bet	8	65	can	40
6	add	1	36	Beth	107	66	cannot	18
7	adds	13	37	big	20	67	cap	3
8	ahh	1	38	bit	13	68	caps	2
9	all	67	39	black	27	69	cash	1
10	am	15	40	blast	1	70	casts	1
11	an	4	41	blasts	2	71	cat	24
12	and	197	42	blend	1	72	cats	7
13	are	60	43	blink	1	73	chant	1
14	as	60	44	blush	2	74	chat	7
15	ask	3	45	bong	3	75	check	17
16	asks	42	46	box	2	76	checks	8
17	at	98	47	brags	1	77	chess	9
18	back	41	48	brass	2	78	chest	1
19	backpack	4	49	brat	3	79	chill	1
20	backup	1	50	bring	14	80	chills	1
21	bad	22	51	brings	1	81	chin	1
22	bag	15	52	brrring	3	82	chips	4
23	bags	25	53	brush	4	83	chop	4
24	ball	49	54	buck	1	84	clap	2
25	band	32	55	bump	1	85	claps	1
26	bangs	1	56	bunk	3	86	clarinet	8
27	bash	1	57	bus	19	87	class	21
28	bath	1	58	but	59	88	clay	4
29	be	76	59	buzz	1	89	clock	2
30	bed	19	60	by	29	90	club	21

#	Word	Count	#	Word	Count	#	Word	Count
91	clubs	4	121	drinks	3	151	fit	2
92	crack	1	122	drips	1	152	fits	1
93	cracks	1	123	drop	3	153	fix	3
94	craft	1	124	drops	2	154	flags	1
95	crafts	2	125	drum	2	155	flash	1
96	crash	1	126	drums	4	156	flat	4
97	crush	2	127	duck	1	157	flip	1
98	cut	2	128	ducks	1	158	flips	1
99	cuts	3	129	dust	1	159	for	69
100	dad	6	130	egg	1	160	forget	6
101	dads	1	131	end	10	161	forgets	3
102	day	41	132	ends	7	162	forgot	1
103	days	7	133	epic	1	163	Fran	14
104	desk	4	134	exist	1	164	frank	2
105	desks	2	135	exit	1	165	frantic	1
106	did	29	136	exits	1	166	fresh	2
107	digs	1	137	expect	6	167	frets	1
108	dim	1	138	expects	1	168	from	10
109	direct	1	139	fact	9	169	front	4
110	discuss	2	140	falls	2	170	fun	27
111	dish	1	141	fan	1	171	fuss	2
112	do	53	142	fans	1	172	gang	2
113	does	55	143	fantastic	1	173	gas	1
114	doll	1	144	fast	13	174	gasps	1
115	down	9	145	fed	1	175	get	54
116	drag	2	146	feels	2	176	gets	30
117	drags	1	147	fell	1	177	Gibbs	66
118	dress	20	148	finish	4	178	gift	2
119	drifts	2	149	Finn	16	179	gig	36
120	drink	4	150	fish	12	180	glad	22

#	Word	Count	#	Word	Count	#	Word	Count
181	glass	2	211	hectic	3	241	i-pods	1
182	go	42	212	hell	1	242	is	228
183	gong	11	213	help	22	243	it	117
184	good	4	214	helps	4	244	its	3
185	got	19	215	her	121	245	Jan	7
186	grab	5	216	hi	5	246	Jill	253
187	grabs	15	217	hill	1	247	job	13
188	grand	28	218	him	3	248	jobs	3
189	grasp	2	219	hints	1	249	jump	4
190	grass	4	220	hip	1	250	jumps	15
191	gray	2	221	hit	2	251	just	50
192	grim	1	222	hits	2	252	kept	1
193	grin	8	223	honk	2	253	kid	2
194	grins	10	224	hops	1	254	kids	29
195	grit	7	225	hot	5	255	kill	1
196	grunt	1	226	how	12	256	kills	1
197	grunts	5	227	hug	2	257	king	2
198	gulp	1	228	hugs	8	258	kiss	1
199	gun	2	229	hums	1	259	lack	1
200	ha	4	230	hunch	1	260	lands	1
201	had	9	231	hut	48	261	lap	5
202	half	6	232	huts	7	262	last	18
203	hand	15	233	I	113	263	left	6
204	hands	5	234	if	23	264	less	2
205	hang	10	235	in	126	265	let	26
206	hangs	1	236	inn	14	266	lets	1
207	has	23	237	intact	1	267	lid	1
208	hat	3	238	intent	1	268	like	40
209	have	60	239	into	16	269	likes	8
210	he	5	240	i-pads	1	270	Lin	196

#	Word	Count
271	lips	2
272	lipstick	2
273	list	9
274	lists	4
275	look	11
276	looks	12
277	lot	6
278	lots	4
279	luck	7
280	lump	1
281	lunch	12
282	lungs	1
283	mad	17
284	man	4
285	map	1
286	math	1
287	may	7
288	me	35
289	mess	6
290	met	1
291	Mills	10
292	Miss	73
293	mix	1
294	mom	21
295	moms	2
296	Monday	2
297	more	11
298	Mr.	7
299	Mrs.	14
300	much	15

#	Word	Count
301	mud	5
302	mug	1
303	must	17
304	my	22
305	nag	3
306	nags	5
307	need	6
308	needs	4
309	next	19
310	no	42
311	nod	1
312	nods	6
313	not	167
314	now	11
315	nut	1
316	nuts	2
317	odd	5
318	of	1
319	off	100
320	oh	18
321	ok	7
322	on	74
323	one	5
324	or	10
325	our	7
326	out	78
327	outfits	1
328	p.m.	1
329	pack	3
330	packs	1

#	Word	Count
331	pact	3
332	pal	6
333	pals	4
334	panic	1
335	panics	1
336	pants	4
337	pass	3
338	past	3
339	path	1
340	pats	2
341	pay	5
342	pests	2
343	pets	1
344	pick	18
345	picks	8
346	picnic	1
347	pinch	1
348	ping	1
349	pink	2
350	PJs	3
351	plan	8
352	play	29
353	plays	3
354	plus	3
355	pond	11
356	pong	1
357	pops	1
358	pot	1
359	prank	3
360	pranks	3

#	Word	Count	#	Word	Count	#	Word	Count
361	prep	4	391	set	33	421	sniffs	8
362	pumpkin	1	392	sets	5	422	snob	1
363	punch	8	393	she	256	423	snug	1
364	pup	2	394	shed	5	424	so	1
365	quick	16	395	shell	1	425	sobs	22
366	rand	4	396	shells	1	426	some	1
367	red	11	397	shh	2	427	speck	1
368	rest	22	398	shock	13	428	spend	2
369	rich	2	399	shot	1	429	spent	6
370	rid	1	400	shrugs	7	430	spins	2
371	rings	2	401	sick	1	431	spirit	1
372	rip	1	402	Sid	132	432	splash	4
373	rips	1	403	silk	4	433	splendid	2
374	rob	1	404	sings	2	434	split	1
375	rock	30	405	sit	4	435	spot	2
376	rocks	2	406	sits	12	436	spots	4
377	rod	4	407	six	19	437	sprints	5
378	rods	1	408	skill	2	438	stab	4
379	run	15	409	skills	4	439	stack	1
380	runs	19	410	skip	7	440	staff	1
381	rush	6	411	skips	1	441	stand	1
382	sad	12	412	slip	1	442	stands	13
383	same	1	413	slips	3	443	stay	8
384	sat	1	414	slot	3	444	stays	14
385	say	14	415	slots	1	445	step	2
386	says	72	416	small	13	446	steps	3
387	scrub	1	417	smells	2	447	stick	5
388	sec	1	418	snack	3	448	sticks	2
389	self-help	1	419	snacks	2	449	stiff	3
390	send	1	420	snaps	3	450	still	1

#	Word	Count	#	Word	Count	#	Word	Count
451	stink	27	481	that	4	511	unpack	1
452	stinks	3	482	the	69	512	until	18
453	stop	14	483	their	440	513	up	72
454	stops	3	484	them	17	514	upset	5
455	string	1	485	then	11	515	us	24
456	stuck	10	486	there	21	516	van	12
457	stuff	4	487	these	35	517	vest	1
458	stuns	3	488	they	4	518	visit	2
459	such	14	489	thing	62	519	Viv	3
460	sum	1	490	things	17	520	wall	2
461	sun	18	491	think	8	521	want	18
462	sunset	1	492	thinks	20	522	wants	20
463	swim	1	493	this	36	523	was	20
464	swims	1	494	thrill	104	524	way	21
465	swing	1	495	ticks	2	525	we	39
466	tablet	1	496	time	1	526	well	31
467	tablets	4	497	tipi	33	527	went	1
468	tag	1	498	tips	1	528	were	10
469	tall	1	499	to	260	529	wet	1
470	task	3	500	top	7	530	what	40
471	tasks	3	501	track	1	531	when	35
472	tell	9	502	trash	7	532	where	6
473	tells	14	503	trick	3	533	whiz	2
474	ten	2	504	tricks	1	534	who	2
475	test	1	505	trip	3	535	why	11
476	text	1	506	trips	2	536	will	90
477	texts	1	507	trumpet	1	537	win	2
478	than	3	508	trunk	3	538	wind	1
479	thank	1	509	trust	6	539	winks	3
480	thanks	1	510	trusts	2	540	wish	3

#	Word	Count
541	with	95
542	yell	7
543	yells	16
544	yelps	2
545	yes	11
546	yet	6
547	you	161
548	your	28
549	yuck	3
550	zip	1
Total Words		**8476**

WANT TO READ MORE
CHAPTER BOOKS

STUDY GUIDES
AND
HANDBOOKS

www.simplewordsbooks.com

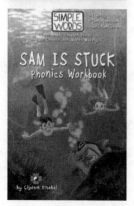

VISIT OUR WEBSITE FOR FREE RESOURCES

simplewordsbooks.com

AND CHECK OUT OUR FREE ONLINE SUMMITS

Made in the USA
San Bernardino, CA
15 March 2020